How to use this book

Follow the advice, in italics, given for you on each page.
Support the children as they read the text that is shaded in cream.
Praise *the children at every step!*

Detailed guidance is provided in the Read Write Inc. *Handbook*

7 reading activities

Children:

- *practise reading the speed sounds*
- *read the green and red words for the story*
- *listen as you read the introduction*
- *discuss the vocabulary check with you*
- *read the story*
- *re-read the story and discuss the 'questions to talk about'*
- *practise reading the speed words*

D0547535

Read
Write Inc.

An inclusive literacy programme by Ruth Miskin

Speed sounds

Consonants *Say the pure sounds (do not add 'uh')*

f ff	l ll	m	n	r	s	v ve	z s	sh	(th)	(ng) (nk)

b	c k (ck)	d	g	h	j	p	qu	t	w wh	x	y	(ch) tch

Vowels *Say the sounds in and out of order*

at	hen	in	on	up	day	see	high	blow	zoo

*Each box contains one sound but sometimes more than one grapheme. Focus graphemes are **circled**.*

Green words

spin   six   stu<u>ck</u>   bla<u>ck</u>   flat   pi<u>nk</u>   lo<u>ng</u>   <u>th</u>in
<u>th</u>em   mun<u>ch</u>   <u>th</u>is

can`not   →   ca<u>nn</u>ot

sit   →   si<u>tt</u>ing   bug   →   bugs
spot   →   spots   wi<u>ng</u>   →   wi<u>ng</u>s

Red words

s<u>ai</u>d   <u>the</u>   my   <u>are</u>

5

Vocabulary check

Discuss the meaning (as used in the story) after the children have read each word.

definition:

bug   *insect*

web   *a spider's trap to catch insects to eat*
        (a bug is stuck in my web)

Punctuation to note in this story:

Spin	*Capital letter for the spider's name*
This But	*Capital letters that start sentences*
.	*Full stop at the end of each sentence*
!	*Exclamation mark used to show anger and surprise*
....	*Wait and see*

The web

Introduction

A spider is sitting on his web, gleefully counting all the bugs he has caught. Will he manage to eat them?

Things do not go as well as he was expecting.

Story written by Gill Munton
Illustrated by Tim Archbold

This is Spin.

Spin is sitting in his web.

"Six bugs are stuck in my web," said Spin.

"A big black bug ...

... a bug with spots ...

... a flat pink bug ...

... a bug with six wings ...

... a fat red bug ...

... and a long thin bug.

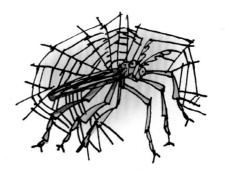

I will get the six bugs and munch them up!"

But ...

"I cannot stand up!"
said Spin.

"I am stuck
in my web!"

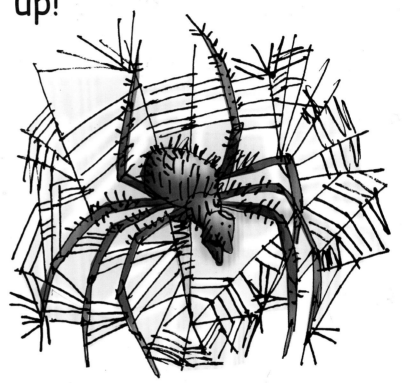

Questions to talk about

FIND IT QUESTIONS

✓ *Turn to the page*

✓ *Read the question to the children*

✓ *Find the answer*

Page 8-9:   *What does Spin say?*
                 What is Spin thinking?

Page 10-11: *Describe all the different bugs.*

Page 12:   *What does Spin plan to do?*
                 Which word tells us this?

Page 13:   *Why can't Spin stand up?*
                 What do you think he is feeling now?